Piano Exam Pieces

ABRSM Grade 5

Selected from the 2019 & 2020 syllabus

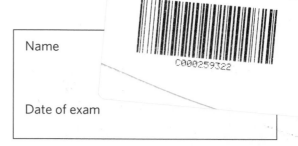

Name

Date of exam

C000259322

Contents

(CD)

page

Editor for ABRSM: Richard Jones

Other pieces for Grade 5

First published in 2018 by ABRSM (Publishing) Ltd,
a wholly owned subsidiary of ABRSM, 4 London Wall Place,
London EC2Y 5AU, United Kingdom
© 2018 by The Associated Board of the Royal Schools of Music
Distributed worldwide by Oxford University Press

Unauthorized photocopying is illegal
All rights reserved. No part of this publication
may be reproduced, recorded or transmitted
in any form or by any means without the
prior permission of the copyright owner.

Music origination by Julia Bovee
Cover by Kate Benjamin & Andy Potts, with thanks to Brighton College
Printed in England by Caligraving Ltd, Thetford, Norfolk, on materials
from sustainable sources.

Aria

Fourth movement from Partita No. 4 in D, BWV 828

J. S. Bach
(1685–1750)

Bach's *Clavierübung*, Part I (1731), consists of six partitas (dance suites), alternating between the French and Italian styles of the day. This is particularly clear in the intermezzi: lightweight dances inserted towards the end of each suite. Among them are a French air and an Italian aria – not vocal imitations but melodious instrumental pieces.

The Aria from Partita No. 4, selected here, has a simple texture, cut-off cadences (e.g. b. 4), and thematic syncopations, often in chains, which are typical of the pre-Classical *galant* style that swept Europe from the 1720s onwards. Dynamics are left to the player's discretion.

Source: *Clavier Übung, Op. 1* (Leipzig: Author, 1731)

© 2018 by The Associated Board of the Royal Schools of Music

A:2

Andante in A

Hob. I:53/II

Joseph Haydn
(1732–1809)

From about 1774, following his *Sturm und Drang* (Storm and Stress) period, Haydn developed a lighter, more popular style, clearly influenced by contemporary opera buffa. One example of this new style is Symphony No. 53, *L'impériale*, from which this Andante was transcribed. It became one of his most successful symphonies, especially in England.

This Andante illustrates the double variations form that Haydn often used: variations on major and tonic minor themes alternate with one another. However, this piano transcription is abridged, so that it contains only three sections – major, minor, major.

Source: *Différentes petites pièces faciles et agréables* (Vienna: Artaria, 1786). The opening dynamic is from Symphony No. 53; the others are editorial. The following slurs are editorial additions: bb. 4, 10 (LH), 31, 36, 40 (LH), 58 (both). All slurs to appoggiaturas are editorial.

8

Minuetto

Fifth movement from Suite No. 6 in E flat

J. B. Loeillet
(1680–1730)

Jean Baptiste Loeillet was born in Ghent, into a family of musicians. He built up a reputation in France as a flautist and composer, but in about 1705 he moved to London, where he became known as 'Mr John Loeillet'. In London he played in orchestras at Drury Lane and the Queen's Theatre, Haymarket, and became well known as a harpsichord player and teacher.

   This Minuetto is selected from the last of Loeillet's Six Suites of 1723. As its name suggests, it belongs to the quicker Italian version of the dance. In line with this style, it is an attractively lively and animated movement, with running semiquavers and much interaction between the hands.

Source: *Six Suits of Lessons for the Harpsicord or Spinnet* (London: J. Walsh, 1723)
The original title of this movement, 'Minuet', is not English, but an abbreviation of the Italian 'Minuetto'. All dynamics are editorial suggestions only, as are accidentals to ornaments.

Chat

Plauderei

No. 1 from *Plaudereien*, Op. 60

Theodor Kirchner
(1823–1903)

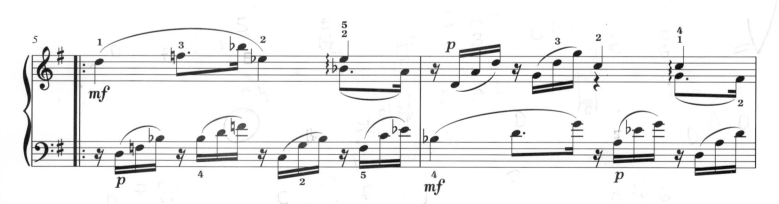

The German composer Theodor Kirchner studied in Leipzig, where he met and was encouraged by Schumann and Mendelssohn. He worked as an organist and teacher in the Swiss towns of Winterthur and Zurich, and later taught at the Würzburg and Dresden conservatories.

Kirchner wrote about 1,000 compositions for piano, many of which are short character-pieces in the style of Schumann. In this piece, from *Plaudereien* (Chats), Op. 60, the two hands engage in an amicable conversation. The left hand (bb. 3–4) imitates the right (bb. 1–2), as if in perfect agreement with it; and later phrases are started by one hand and finished by the other (bb. 6, 9 and 10). **The first repeat should be observed in the exam.**

Source: *Plaudereien: 25 Stücke für Klavier, Op. 60* (Berlin: Simrock, 1882). The **mf** in b. 9 is editorial (cf. b. 10).

B:2

Étude in A minor

No. 2 from *25 études faciles*, Op. 50

Louise Farrenc
(1804–75)

The French pianist Louise Farrenc composed many piano and chamber-music pieces, and was for over 30 years professor of piano at the Paris Conservatoire (1842–73). She and her husband edited a 23-volume anthology of early keyboard music, *Le trésor des pianistes* (The Pianists' Treasury). This étude imitates the siciliana, a pastoral type of piece in slowish compound time with dotted rhythms, which became very popular in the early 18th century. The étude is in ABA[1] form, with a middle section that starts in the relative major C (b. 9), a varied reprise (b. 19), and a coda (b. 26).

Source: *25 Études progressives pour le piano, Op. 50* (Paris: Leduc, 1876). The dynamics in the following bars are editorial suggestions only: bb. 1, 4–5, 8, 22–3, 25–6, as is the poco rit. in b. 30.

The Harp Player

Joueur de harpe

No. 8 from *Bagatelles*, Op. 34

Jean Sibelius
(1865–1957)

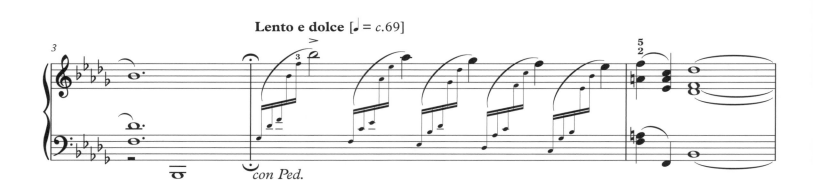

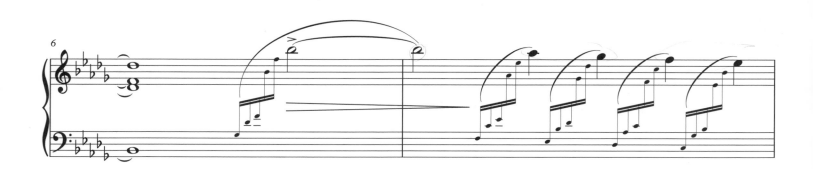

The great Finnish composer Jean Sibelius wrote over 150 short piano pieces during a period of 40 years (1889–1929). The majority of them are accessible, intimate, romantic salon pieces – a genre that was much in demand at the time.

Sibelius's *Bagatelles*, Op. 34, composed in 1912–16, contains ten miniatures with fanciful or dance titles. In 'Joueur de harpe', the arpeggios imitate the harpist plucking the strings. 'Stretto' (bb. 1 and 8) denotes a quickening of the speed.

Source: Jean Sibelius Archive, MS Collections (Catalogue No. 0038), National Library of Finland

© Fennica Gehrman Oy, Helsinki

The Schoolmaster

Rektor

No. 12 from *Melodie ludowe*

Witold Lutosławski
(1913–94)

From 1945 onwards, the Polish composer Witold Lutosławski made much use of folk tunes in his compositions, notably in his well-known Concerto for Orchestra. In 1945 itself, he arranged for the piano 12 *Melodie ludowe* (Folk Melodies) that were drawn from different regions of Poland.

　　No. 12, selected here, is based on a folk dance from Silesia in south-west Poland. The folk tune is built into an ABA[1] structure, consisting of melody (bb. 1–17), variation (18–34), varied reprise (35–51), and coda (53–60). Although the composer's metronome mark is ♩ = 168, students may prefer a more relaxed tempo of ♩ = c.138.

C:2

Lentamente

No. 1 from *Visions fugitives*, Op. 22

Sergey Prokofiev
(1891–1953)

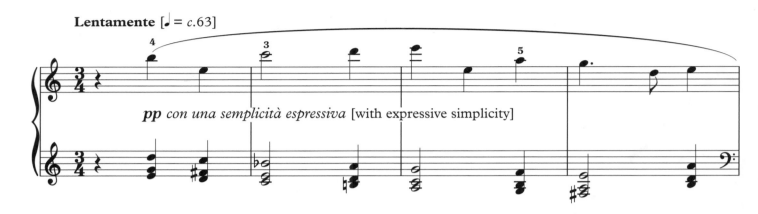

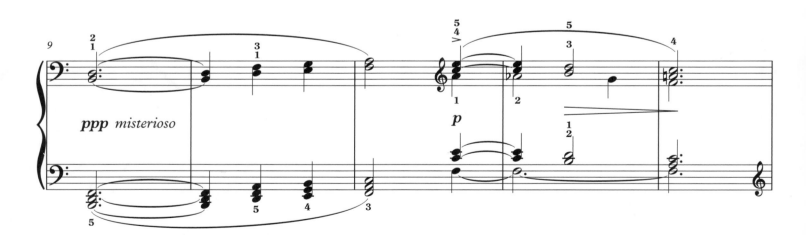

When very young, the Russian composer Sergey Prokofiev showed extraordinary talent both in piano playing and in composition. First taught by his mother, herself a pianist, he was writing his earliest piano pieces by the age of five.

Visions fugitives (Fleeting Visions), Op. 22, from which this piece is selected, dates from his early Russian period: it contains 20 pieces that were written in 1915–17, during the First World War. The opening item, Lentamente, reveals the dream-like side of Prokofiev's artistic personality.

Source: *Mimoletnosti – Visions fugitives. Nouvelle edition revue par l'auteur* (Moscow: Gutheil, *c.*1925)

© Copyright 1922 by Hawkes & Son (London) Ltd
Published in *Visions Fugitives*, Op. 22 (ISMN 979-0-060-081781).

Film Noir

Mike Cornick
(born 1947)

 C:3

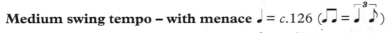

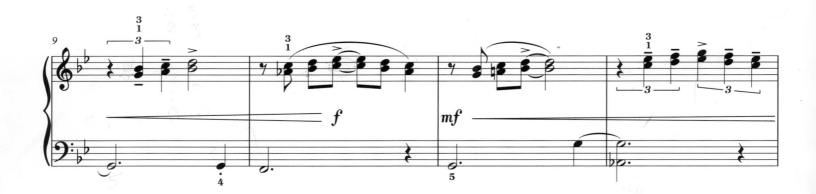

Mike Cornick studied composition at Trinity College of Music, London. He teaches piano and keyboard, and is well known for his jazz piano compositions.

Film noir (black film) is a type of Hollywood crime drama from the 1940s or 1950s. So this piece is rather like film music, using jazz idioms to capture the dark, menacing, melodramatic quality of this specific genre.